THE BUILDINGS OF
ANCIENT GREECE

Helen and Richard Leacroft

WILLIAM R. SCOTT INC. (PUBLISHER) NEW YORK

THE buildings of Ancient Greece are known throughout the world, but those which can be seen today are only the remnants of the great civilization that we call Ancient Greece. To trace the history of earlier buildings and see how they developed we must draw on the evidence provided by archaeologists. They have uncovered great cities like Troy, and palaces such as Mycenae and Tiryns—the homes of the heroes of whom Homer, the Greek poet, wrote in the Iliad *and the* Odyssey—*and have also shown us the facts behind many of the ancient Greek legends.*

Greece is a Mediterranean country, enclosed by the Adriatic, Ionian and Aegean Seas. It is divided by mountain ridges which form barriers between the many small plains. The Greeks lived on the mainland, on the islands of the Aegean, the coast of Asia Minor and even as far west as Southern Italy and Sicily. Summers were long and hot and the people spent much time out of doors, but the winters were cold and wet, so buildings had to provide shade, warmth and protection. This book shows how the Greeks built their homes, temples and the many other buildings which they needed as their way of life developed.

ROUND HUTS: Built either of thatch on a light timber frame, or of mud brick on stone base wall

DEVELOPMENT FROM CIRCULAR HUT: Addition of porch leads to rectangular hut with rounded end (see also drawings on pages 6 and 10)

PREHISTORIC AND MINOAN TIMES

The earliest inhabitants of Greece were wandering tribesmen. At first, like most prehistoric people, their homes were simple round huts made of woven wattles, or sticks, daubed with mud. In northern Greece this sort of 'beehive' hut is still sometimes used. The circular shape, however, was difficult to enlarge, so, as building methods improved, the shape gradually changed, passing through various forms until a rectangular plan was reached. Sometimes a remnant of the circle lingered as a semicircular end to the building. This development did not take place only once, but happened many times as new tribes settled in the country. In later times sun-dried mud bricks were used and many rectangular houses, similar to the ones excavated at Troy in Asia Minor, must have been built.

The mud brick walls set on stone footings, enclosed a single room spanned by wooden poles on which were placed smaller poles and reed matting; the whole roof was then covered with a layer of clay which was thick in the middle and sloped gently to the sides to carry away the rain-water. The roof probably extended beyond the walls to form eaves which protected the mud brick walls from being washed away by the rain, and the stone footings protected them from the water which splashed up from the ground. As the width of houses increased timber posts were used inside the

2

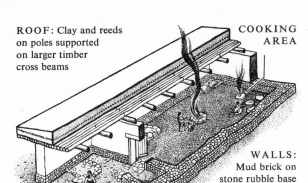

ROOF: Clay and reeds on poles supported on larger timber cross beams

COOKING AREA

WALLS: Mud brick on stone rubble base

HOUSE AT TROY, cir. 2700 B.C.

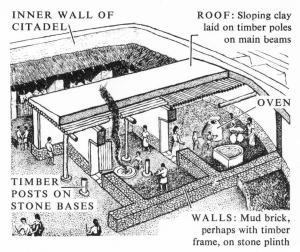

INNER WALL OF CITADEL

ROOF: Sloping clay laid on timber poles on main beams

OVEN

TIMBER POSTS ON STONE BASES

WALLS: Mud brick, perhaps with timber frame, on stone plinth

DIMENI, THESSALY Chieftain's house of the Late Neolithic period, cir. 2500 B.C.

building to help support the roofs. These would certainly have been needed if, as is still done today in the Middle East, extra layers of clay were added to the roof when it leaked. Both the roof and side walls projected forward to make a shady porch where the family could sit. Timber planks were used to protect the ends of the porch walls and the sides and top of the entrance. Stones were usually set across the bottom of the door opening to form a threshold. The fire was on a paved hearth in the middle of the room, while the cooking hearth was set against the back wall. Near by a small pit was often to be found which may have been used for setting the dough for bread. Reed matting covered the floor and the people slept on low stone platforms. When, as at Dimeni, the space was divided into two, the central hearth was in the main living-room, while the rear room with the cooking hearth and food store was most likely the women's place.

Whatever the shape, most houses on the mainland of Greece were individual units, complete in themselves, but even as early as 2000 B.C., the houses on the island of Crete were not free-standing, but were built next door to each other, often sharing walls. Even the simplest had several rooms opening off each other. This more complicated arrangement may well have been influenced by trading contacts with Egypt and other near-eastern countries.

By 1500 B.C., the inhabitants of Crete, now often called Minoans after their legendary King Minos, had developed an advanced civilization. The sea around the island was their defence, and they were able to live in unwalled cities grouped around the palaces of their rulers (page 20). The palaces, such as are to be found at Mallia, Phaestos and Knossos, had many rooms arranged around an open courtyard. Smaller courts, known as light wells, sunk into the mass of the building, provided light and air for the inner rooms.

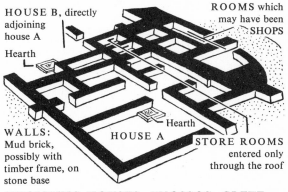

HOUSE B, directly adjoining house A

Hearth

ROOMS which may have been SHOPS

Hearth

WALLS: Mud brick, possibly with timber frame, on stone base

HOUSE A

STORE ROOMS entered only through the roof

NEOLITHIC HOUSES, KNOSSOS, CRETE cir. 2600 B.C. Here cut open to show the many rooms

All the major palaces of Crete had a large courtyard of similar size, and it is thought that this was because they were used for the dangerous sport of bull-leaping in which both young men and girls took part. In the picture above this sport is shown taking place in the palace at Knossos. The building was two, and in some places three, floors high. The ground floor walls were made of stone, but the upper walls were framed with timber and filled in with plastered stone rubble or sun-dried mud brick.

The main approach to this palace was from the west (top left of picture), on this side of the courtyard were the state-rooms, the king's throne room and similar apartments. A staircase led down into the courtyard on the east (bottom) of which were the queen's quarters. On the ground floor there were many storerooms built as long narrow chambers which may well have accounted for the legend of the

4

THE THIRD PALACE AT KNOSSOS, CRETE, circa 1500 B.C.
The ceremony of Bull-leaping takes place in the great Central Court of the Palace

labyrinth in which Thesus is said to have fought the Minotaur. At the top right of the picture is the theatral area where dancing or processions may have taken place, the audience standing or sitting on the stone steps to watch.

The Minoans were gay and peace-loving. Their houses were decorated with frescoes, or wall-paintings, of flowers, birds, animals and fish. Scenes also showed dancers, musicians, and athletes performing the bull-leaping.

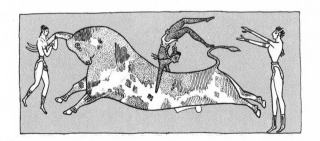

FRESCO from the Palace showing young men and women performing the bull game

5

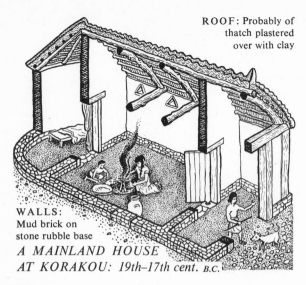

ROOF: Probably of thatch plastered over with clay

WALLS: Mud brick on stone rubble base

A MAINLAND HOUSE AT KORAKOU: 19th–17th cent. B.C.

THE MYCENAEANS

Minoan influence spread to the Greek mainland, and there was an exchange of trade and culture between the Minoans and the people who lived on the mainland at such places as Mycenae, Tiryns and Pylos. The palaces of these people had decorations very similar to those in Cretan palaces. So much so that it is sometimes thought that migrating Minoans had established these settlements; although it is more likely that they were inhabited by the Achaeans, whom nowadays we call Mycenaeans, who had moved down into Greece from the northlands. By 1400 B.C., however, the Minoan civilization on Crete had come to an end, possibly as the result of earthquakes followed by tidal waves. Perhaps the mainlanders took the opportunity to burn and pillage the towns and palaces, and to seize the Minoan trading routes with Egypt and the eastern Mediterranean countries.

Unlike the Minoans, the Mycenaeans did not have the protection of the sea, and the kings built their palaces on hills which they protected with great encircling walls of massive stones. This type of walling is called Cyclopean, because the stones were so huge that later generations thought that a race of giants, known in legends as the Cyclopes, must have built them. The palace had accommodation for the king's family and his retainers, while the homes of the common people were built outside the *acropolis*

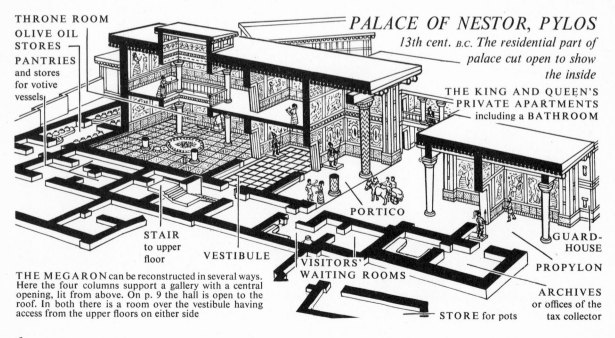

THRONE ROOM
OLIVE OIL STORES
PANTRIES and stores for votive vessels

STAIR to upper floor

VESTIBULE

VISITORS' WAITING ROOMS

PORTICO

PALACE OF NESTOR, PYLOS
13th cent. B.C. The residential part of palace cut open to show the inside

THE KING AND QUEEN'S PRIVATE APARTMENTS including a BATHROOM

GUARD-HOUSE

PROPYLON

ARCHIVES or offices of the tax collector

STORE for pots

THE MEGARON can be reconstructed in several ways. Here the four columns support a gallery with a central opening, lit from above. On p. 9 the hall is open to the roof. In both there is a room over the vestibule having access from the upper floors on either side

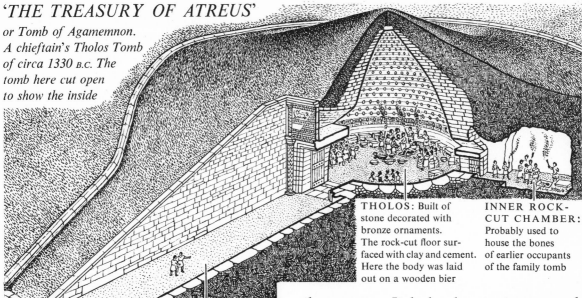

'THE TREASURY OF ATREUS'

or Tomb of Agamemnon.
A chieftain's Tholos Tomb
of circa 1330 B.C. The
tomb here cut open
to show the inside

THOLOS: Built of
stone decorated with
bronze ornaments.
The rock-cut floor sur-
faced with clay and cement.
Here the body was laid
out on a wooden bier

INNER ROCK-
CUT CHAMBER:
Probably used to
house the bones
of earlier occupants
of the family tomb

DROMOS or
entrance passage

WALL to hold
back the earth used to fill the dromos

or fortified citadel; an open space within the
walls provided refuge for them and their animals
in times of trouble.

The construction of the Mycenaean palace was
similar to that of Crete, with stone base walls,
sometimes with stone walled basement rooms,
supporting upper walls of sun-dried bricks or
rubble. The walls were strengthened by timber
posts sunk into grooves built into each side of
the wall and tied together by short beams
running through the thickness of the wall; they
were also tied by additional beams running
along the length of the walls. The walls between
the beams were plastered and painted with
patterns and scenes. In both the Cretan and
Mycenaean buildings the wooden columns were
narrow at the base and wide at the head: it is
sometimes thought that this shape developed
from the use of tree trunks set upside-down so
that the broad base could give wider support to
the roof timbers.

The main building of the palace was called
the *megaron*. It had a large entrance porch
where Homer, who based his stories of the
Trojan War on the Mycenaean civilization, says
that beds for the guests were set. Beyond the
porch was the great shadowy inner hall such as
might have been seen in the palace of Nestor at
Pylos or at Tiryns (page 9).

Underneath one of the smaller megara at
Tiryns the remains of a chieftain's circular house
were found. Although the circular house was no
longer in general use, the shape was still kept for
the homes of the noble dead. These *tholoi*, as
they were called, were built within round holes
cut into the hillsides, and a level way—*dromos*—
flanked by great stone retaining walls led into
them. In the hole a great circular stone dome
was constructed by slightly projecting the stones
of each course, or layer, in front of the course
beneath; a method of building known as corbel-
ling. The inside face of each course was cut to a
curve until a beehive shape was made. The
door opening, some fifteen feet high, was spanned by a stone lintel, protected from the weight
above by a triangular 'arch'. When the burial
was complete the whole structure was covered
over with earth, and the dromos filled in.

7

THE PALACE AND CITADEL,
TIRYNS. 1400–1200 B.C.

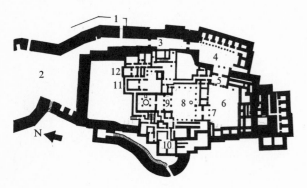

The fortress or citadel at Tiryns was built and
added to for over a hundred years. In its final
form the main entrance (1) was on the east side
leading to an open area (2) where the local
population could take shelter, or through a
passage which could easily be defended
(3) into a courtyard (4) with a row of stores.
Two columned entrance porticoes—*propylaea*—
(5, 7) led to the outer (6) and inner (8) courts,
the latter leading directly to the great Megaron

(9). To the east of this lay two smaller megara (11; 12), one of which may have been the women's quarters. Additional rooms (10) may have been used as bed, bath and store rooms.

Inside the Megaron four wooden columns surrounded the central hearth upon which braziers holding burning logs were set. The walls were richly decorated with paintings. The floor, except for the low dais for the throne, was divided into squares ornamented with dolphins, octopuses and other decorations. According to Homer, the golden entrance doors hung on silver posts and swung over a bronze threshold. In the evening the king sat on his inlaid throne, while the queen and her women spun and wove their yarn, and the community feasted and were entertained with music and dancing. Homer describes many of these features in the *Odyssey*, and archaeologists have found evidence to confirm his descriptions.

Early Temples

During the twelfth century B.C., throughout the whole Mediterranean area there was a great upheaval of peoples, known as the Great Migration. In Greece the Mycenaeans were overthrown by tribes from the north, among them the Dorians, who settled in the Peloponnese. Although some Mycenaeans probably remained and lived alongside the new settlers, others set sail and founded colonies on the islands and the mainland to the east. For the next three centuries there is a black-out on information and no records have been found, but by the eighth century B.C., the civilization of what we know as Classical Greece had started to emerge.

Each group of people now lived in an independent community or city-state—*polis*. Each polis had its own laws, customs and gods. In earlier times the king, living in his megaron, had been looked on as a god, and so the temples, the homes for the new gods, developed from the palace megaron. The builders continued to use mud brick and timber, and both pitched and flat roofs were found, as may be seen from the

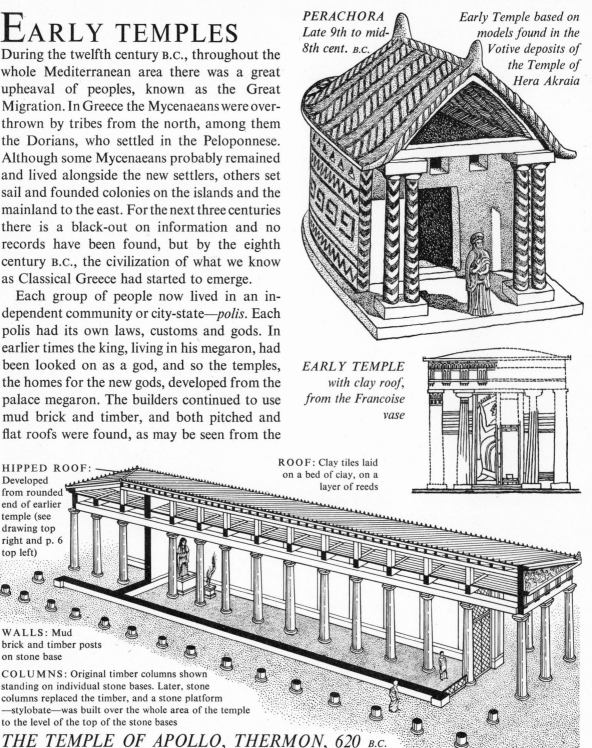

PERACHORA Late 9th to mid-8th cent. B.C.

Early Temple based on models found in the Votive deposits of the Temple of Hera Akraia

EARLY TEMPLE with clay roof, from the Francoise vase

HIPPED ROOF: Developed from rounded end of earlier temple (see drawing top right and p. 6 top left)

ROOF: Clay tiles laid on a bed of clay, on a layer of reeds

WALLS: Mud brick and timber posts on stone base

COLUMNS: Original timber columns shown standing on individual stone bases. Later, stone columns replaced the timber, and a stone platform —stylobate—was built over the whole area of the temple to the level of the top of the stone bases

THE TEMPLE OF APOLLO, THERMON, 620 B.C.

drawings on the left. The round-ended clay model has a high-pitched roof, possibly of timber and thatch covered with clay, while the vase painting of a temple shows a slightly sloping flat clay roof. This example also shows that the planks protecting the ends of the side walls (page 3) have now become decorative *antae* and the two columns set between—*in antis*—have fluting carved down their length, while further decoration has been added across the top of the building.

As time went on, a low-pitched roof was to become the main type. These roofs were covered with interlocking baked clay—terracotta—tiles, bedded in clay on a layer of reeds; later marble tiles were to be used. Horizontal beams, resting on the walls and on posts standing on great bearer beams spanning the building, carried roof rafters. The width of the building was limited by the size and strength of the timber available for beams, but it could be increased by the use of additional posts: at first a single row down the middle and later two rows. Extra posts added around the outside of the building supported the larger overhanging eaves, and made a pleasantly shaded walking way.

In the Temple of Apollo, Thermon, the ends of the bearer beams were protected from the weather by terracotta panels—*triglyphs*—ornamented with vertical grooves, while the space between the beams was filled with mud brick walling faced with decorated terracotta panels—*metopes*. Later, although these panels were no longer needed for protection, they remained as decoration, and were repeated across the ends of the building as well as along the sides, providing the additional decoration already noted above. The edges of the roofs were protected by terracotta cornices and rain-water spouts were modelled in the form of animal heads.

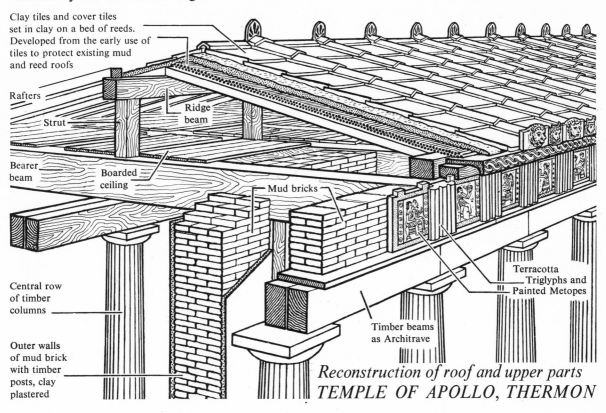

Clay tiles and cover tiles set in clay on a bed of reeds. Developed from the early use of tiles to protect existing mud and reed roofs

Rafters

Strut

Ridge beam

Bearer beam

Boarded ceiling

Mud bricks

Central row of timber columns

Outer walls of mud brick with timber posts, clay plastered

Mud bricks

Terracotta Triglyphs and Painted Metopes

Timber beams as Architrave

Reconstruction of roof and upper parts
TEMPLE OF APOLLO, THERMON

11

ALTAR

VOTIVE
COLUMN

PROPYLAEUM
OR GATEWAY

TEMENOS
OR SACRED
ENCLOSURE

VE OF
HAIA

THE INSIDE OF A TEMPLE AND ITS SURROUNDINGS
The Sanctuary of Aphaia on the island of Aegina, circa 500 B.C.

The Ancient Greeks believed that many features of the landscape such as springs, wells, groves, rocks or caves had a spirit living in them, and the ground around was considered sacred. Sometimes they built a shrine or temple as a home for the spirit. Such a spirit was Aphaia who, around 2000 B.C., was thought to live in a small cave on the island of Aegina. At first an altar in the open air was built in her honour, but as religion developed and the spirits came to be

thought of as being very like, but greater tha. humans, a more fitting home was needed and so a temple was built. Over the years the first simple buildings were replaced by others of more magnificence. Three temples were built for Aphaia, each larger and finer than the one before, and the illustration shows the third temple to be built on the site at the beginning of the fifth century B.C.

The sacred area—*temenos*—was surrounded

OPISTH-ODOMUS here it is used as a treasury or adytum

CELLA OR NAOS

TEMENOS OR SACRED ENCLOSURE

PTEROMA OR PASSAGEWAY

PERISTYLE OR COLONNADE

by a wall, and the worshippers entered through a covered gateway—*propylaeum*—into the sanctuary. In the open space a sacrificial altar stood before the east front of the temple. The Greeks did not use the inside of the temple building for public worship as a modern church is used, for it was the home of the deity whose statue was placed in the main room—*cella or naos*—facing the entrance. Here there was a small altar for personal offerings brought by pilgrims, and people could take sanctuary here under the protection of the deity. At the front an open porch —*pronaos*—led to the cella, behind which there was sometimes an inner room—*adytum*—which served as a private apartment for the god or goddess, and also as a store for goods or money belonging to the temple, or deposited there for safe keeping. Sometimes, as here, a rear porch—*opisthodomus*—enclosed by bronze gates, was used for this purpose.

13

TEMPLE OF APHAIA,
AEGINA: View in the
interior of the naos

The typical large temple had two rows of columns in the cella to support the roof, and often these were arranged on two levels. This made it possible to use smaller columns which took up less floor space, and were more in scale with the enclosed space than a single full height column would have been.

The deity was served by citizens chosen by lot: these priests and priestesses performed the sacrifices, delivered and interpreted the oracles by which the gods gave advice to those who sought it, and cared for the daily life of the god or goddess. At festival times, processions singing hymns walked into the temenos, sacrifices were offered, and feasting, dancing and athletic competitions took place. Particular sanctuaries became renowned for special festivals: Olympia for the games, Delphi for its oracle and music, and Epidaurus for medicine. People travelled from all over Greece to take part and compete in the festivals, for many of the tribal deities were now worshipped by all the Greeks.

14

CLASSICAL GREECE

During the late sixth and fifth centuries B.C., stone replaced the use of timber and brick for building temples because it was a more durable material. However, the traditional shapes of the timber and terracotta details were faithfully reproduced, although the height, width and spacing of the columns varied enormously, depending upon the strength of the stone being used. At first the columns were tall and slim in imitation of a timber post, but as the timber architraves (page 11) and cornices were replaced by heavy stone, so the columns became thick, short and closely spaced. It was about 490 B.C. that the Athenian Treasury at Delphi (on the right in the picture on the title page) was built in marble, a stone which enabled the masons to carve fine mouldings and decorations. By the middle of the fifth century B.C., the Dorian architects were paying particular attention to the correction of optical illusions. Unlike those of Crete and Mycenae, the columns which they used tapered towards the top. However, when seen against the sky, a straight-sided column would appear to be too thin in the middle, so to correct this impression the columns were given an *enthasis*, that is they were curved slightly outwards along their length. To create a greater feeling of strength the columns were built to lean slightly inwards, and at the corners of the building they were thickened and placed closer together. When the corner columns were moved, however, the pattern of triglyph directly over the column with square metopes between was broken, and many variations had to be tried before a satisfactory solution was achieved. The *stylobate* or platform on which the building stood, was built to curve upwards from the corners to the middle of each side and to the

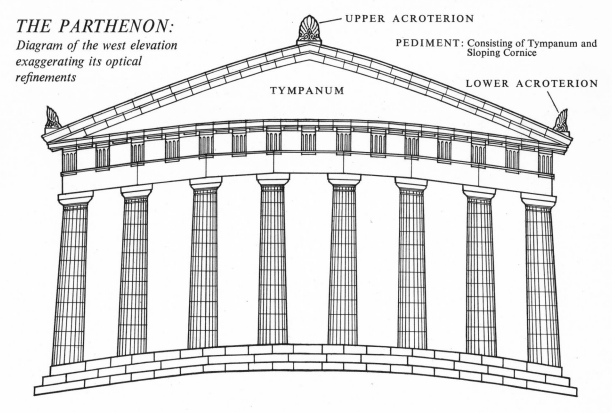

THE PARTHENON:

Diagram of the west elevation exaggerating its optical refinements

UPPER ACROTERION

PEDIMENT: Consisting of Tympanum and Sloping Cornice

TYMPANUM

LOWER ACROTERION

15

middle of the building; this did away with any impression of sagging that a flat stylobate might have given. As all the columns were the same height the whole of the upper parts of the temple had to curve in the same way; the masons needed great skill to set out these curves, and to cut each stone so that it fitted exactly.

The foundations of the temples were built very carefully, the ground often being excavated to considerable depths to find a solid base. The stones were brought from the quarries on wheeled carts drawn by oxen and lifted into position by means of ropes and pulleys, the ropes being held in place beneath bosses—projections —left on the stones. Other raising methods involved cutting horseshoe shaped grooves in the ends of the stones into which ropes could be fitted, or using lifting wedges which were set in a hole in the top of the stone. On larger temples when enormous stones were used, many oxen

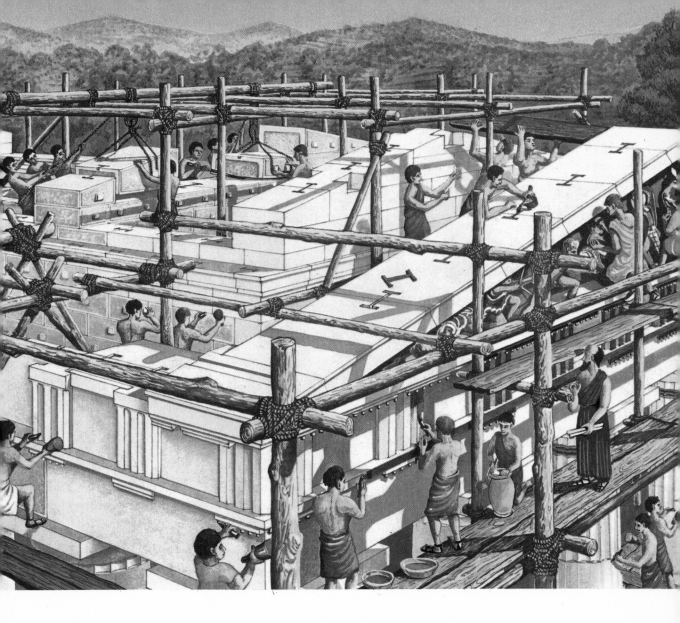

had to be yoked together to draw the carts and more complicated lifting devices were used.

The drums of the columns were centered above each other by means of a small wooden pin set into a bronze or wooden plug sunk into the upper face of the stone. No mortar was used between the joints, but sometimes metal clamps and dowels helped to hold the stones in position. To prevent the surface of the stones from being damaged while building operations were going on, the final dressing of the stonework was completed after the roughly cut stones had been placed in position. When they built a temple the Greeks began with the outer colonnade, and moved inwards to the cella. The sculpture, ready for painting, was the last thing to be placed in position. In the picture it has been necessary to show many of the building operations taking place at the same time, so that it is possible to see how they were carried out.

17

TEMPLE OF ARTEMIS, EPHESUS, cir. 550 B.C. after A. S. Murray

By the eighth century B.C., those Greeks who had left the mainland and had settled along the coast of Asia Minor and the adjoining islands had set up great towns such as Ephesus and Miletus. These people had become known as Ionians, and they developed their own forms of art and architecture, both of which owed a great deal to the arts of the neighbouring peoples of Phoenicia, Assyria and Egypt. The mainland Dorians were also great colonizers, and they carried their ideas and architectural forms across the seas. Many of their finest buildings are to be found in such places as Sicily and Southern Italy, as well as on the coast of Asia Minor.

The architecture produced by the Dorians is known as Doric, and that of the Ionians as Ionic; both forms developed at much the same time, with the result that they affected each

other, at any rate in minor details. In 477 B.C., after the Persian Wars, Athens and many of the city states, not only on the mainland, but also on the Aegean islands and the coast of Asia Minor, formed a league, known as the Delian League, to ensure that the Persians should never again attack Greece. Gradually, under the leadership of Pericles, Athens became the leader of the League, and it was to uphold her position that she started to rebuild the temples on the Acropolis. As a result it is here that we can find some of the finest examples of each style of architecture: the Parthenon in the Doric, and the Erechtheum in a simplified Ionic style.

The actual shapes of the temples in both forms were very similar, except that the larger Ionic temples often had two rows of columns surrounding the cella. The Ionic column stands

18

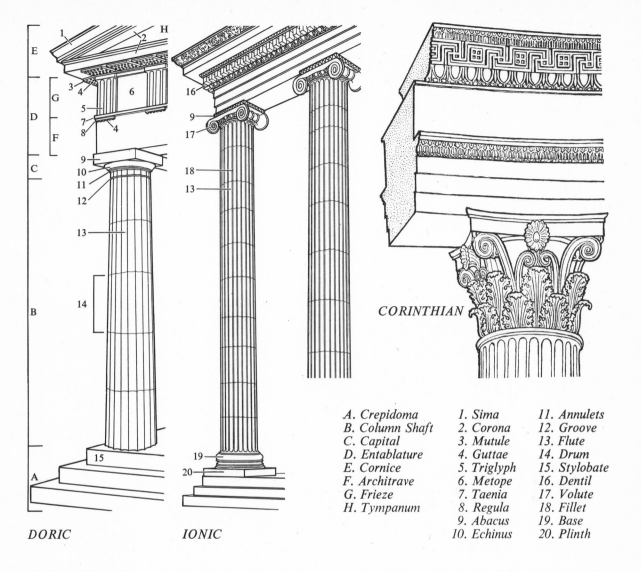

A. Crepidoma	1. Sima	11. Annulets
B. Column Shaft	2. Corona	12. Groove
C. Capital	3. Mutule	13. Flute
D. Entablature	4. Guttae	14. Drum
E. Cornice	5. Triglyph	15. Stylobate
F. Architrave	6. Metope	16. Dentil
G. Frieze	7. Taenia	17. Volute
H. Tympanum	8. Regula	18. Fillet
	9. Abacus	19. Base
	10. Echinus	20. Plinth

DORIC   IONIC

CORINTHIAN

upon a base above the stylobate, and it is slimmer than the Doric column, but it is in their decoration that the main differences are to be found, as may be seen by comparing the drawings of the architectural orders in the diagram above. The most obvious difference is seen in the capital, the Ionic having a spiral scroll or *volute*. Neither triglyphs nor metopes were used on an Ionic building, but dentils are to be seen representing what in earlier buildings would have been the small roof timbers supporting the overhanging eaves.

A variation on the Ionic order was the Corinthian, which had a capital with volutes combined with a stylized pattern of acanthus leaves. This style, however, was used only sparingly by the Greeks, but was later to become a favourite with the Romans. Colour played an important part in all Greek buildings. It was applied to the architectural details in the upper parts of the building, and the colouring of the sculpture was lifelike.

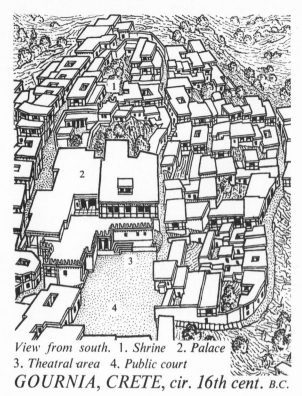

View from south. 1. *Shrine* 2. *Palace*
3. *Theatral area* 4. *Public court*
GOURNIA, CRETE, *cir. 16th cent.* B.C.

TOWNS

In Minoan and Mycenaean times towns grew up in a haphazard manner around the palace or citadel, their layout being influenced largely by the nature of the land on which they were built. When protective walls were needed they followed the lay of the land. This informal arrangement persisted, especially on the mainland, but by the fifth century B.C., the Ionians had introduced a system of town planning for new cities. They used a grid-iron plan with the streets crossing each other at right angles, producing a series of rectangular blocks for the buildings and open spaces. This plan was applied to flat and hilly sites alike, and in the latter case the minor streets were often no more than stairways.

The central feature of every town was an open space called the *agora*, where all the citizens could meet together to discuss the problems of the community, pass the time of day and purchase their food and other necessities.

1. *Acropolis* 2. *Sanctuary of Demeter* 3. *Theatre* 4. *Upper Gymnasium* 5. *Council Hall, for interior see pages 28–9* 6. *Sanctuary of Athena* 7. *Agora* 8. *Sanctuary of Zeus* 9. *Lower Gymnasium* 10. *Stadium*

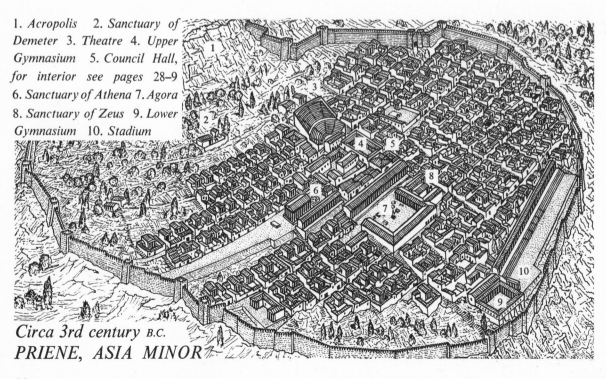

Circa 3rd century B.C.
PRIENE, ASIA MINOR

INTERIOR OF STOA OF ATTALOS, ATHENS, late 3rd cent. B.C. (see No. 11, page 22)

As a democratic system developed in each polis, new civic buildings were needed and these were grouped around the agora. Democracy means government by the people and the polis was an independent city-state made up of the people living not only in the actual town but in the surrounding countryside, who banded themselves together for political unity and trade. As every man had an obligation to take part in the government of the polis, Aristotle (384–322 B.C.) thought it important that towns should be of such a size that all the citizens could know each other's personal character when civic duties had

to be allotted, yet at the same time there must be enough people to do all the work needed in the fields and town to provide for the 'good life'.

The most characteristic building in the agora was an open colonnade or *stoa*, consisting of a row of columns in front of a wall, with a connecting roof to provide shade for the people who strolled or sat beneath. Many stoas, like that of Attalos, now reconstructed in the Athenian Agora, were two columns deep and two floors high. Sometimes rooms were built at the rear and served as offices or shops, and in at least one case the stoa was used as a picture gallery.

ACROPOLIS

1

2

3

4

5

6

7

8

9

10

AREOPAGUS

25

26

27

11

AGORA

24

18

19

23

22

KOLONOS
AGORAIOS

12

13

17

16

21

20

14

15

The relationship between city, agora and acropolis may clearly be seen in Athens during the classical period. Athens was not built on the grid system but developed around the Acropolis. Originally a Mycenaean hill-top citadel, the Acropolis became a religious precinct with many temples. Chief among these was the Parthenon—Home of the Maiden—dedicated to the city goddess, Athena. The Acropolis walls were entered through the Propylaea (see cover) which dominated the approach along the Panathenaic Way. This road was named after the procession which took place annually when a new robe was presented to the statue of Athena.

Around the Agora were stoas and civic buildings, including the Council House and the Town Hall. In this hall banquets were held and important visitors received, and here the sacred city hearth was found on which a fire always burned, symbolizing the life of the city. The

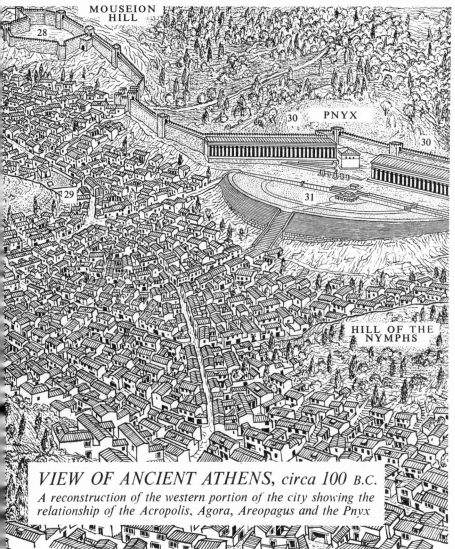

MOUSEION HILL

28

PNYX

30

30

29

31

HILL OF THE NYMPHS

VIEW OF ANCIENT ATHENS, circa 100 B.C.
A reconstruction of the western portion of the city showing the relationship of the Acropolis, Agora, Areopagus and the Pnyx

1. *Parthenon*
2. *Erechtheum*
3. *Site of old temple of Athena*
4. *Propylaea*
5. *Temple of Nike Apteros*
6. *Klepsydra – sacred spring*
7. *Eleusinion, home of the mysteries*
8. *Mint*
9. *South-east fountain house*
10. *Panathenaic Way*
11. *Stoa of Attalos*
12. *Painted stoa*
13. *Temenos of the 12 Gods*
14. *Stoa of the Herms*
15. *Stoa of Zeus*
16. *Temple of Zeus & Athena*
17. *Temple of Apollo Patroos*
18. *The Eponymous Heroes*
19. *Metroon and state archives*
20. *Temple of Hephaestus*
21. *Bouleuterion – council hall*
22. *Fountain house*
23. *Tholos, used as town hall*
24. *Middle stoa*
25. *South stoa*
26. *Heliaia – legal court*
27. *South-west fountain house*
28. *Mouseion fort*
29. *Sanctuary of Dionysus*
30. *Pnyx, east and west stoas, here shown as intended*
31. *Meeting place of the General Assembly*

Agora also contained temples, shrines, altars and fountain houses. These were not only shrines to the water deities, but were also the main source of water, as this was not usually piped to individual houses.

In early times the citizens held political discussions in the Agora, but later they moved to the Pnyx. Here an orator stood with his back to the Agora and addressed an audience standing facing him on the side of the hill, but by the fifth century B.C. the positions had been reversed by the building of an artificial slope on the hillside above. Public meetings, however, were still held in the Agora; for example, the ceremony of ostracism at which a citizen guilty of a crime against the polis could be exiled. The chief magistrates held their meetings on the hill of the Areopagus, which had many religious connections; early tombs have been found on the site, and St Paul preached there in A.D. 53.

23

PANATHENAIC PROCESSION: Figures from the north and west friezes of the Parthenon

The illustration shows a view of the Athenian Agora from the Stoa of Attalos, with the Panathenaic procession making its way up to the Acropolis.

In every city the merchants, tradesmen and bankers all had their quarters around the agora as did the fish-sellers, butchers and the vendors of pottery, bronzes and slaves. These market areas were probably like those of many European market-towns, with the tradesmen shouting

their wares and prices from the shop fronts or open stalls and bargaining with their customers. It was the master of the house, or if he were very important, his chief steward, who rose at dawn and went to the market early in the morning to buy for his household, a slave carrying the purchases home. There must have been the usual mess and litter from street markets, because special officials were appointed to see that all was kept clean and tidy, and also that merchants dealt honestly with their customers.

Mixed in with this haggling throng were those who had come to the agora to meet their friends, sit over a drink, gossip or exchange the latest scandal. Not all the talk was on such an everyday level, however, for here such men as Socrates (470–399 B.C.) gathered their disciples around them, and the use of the stoa as a place of discussion by Zeno (340–264 B.C.) and his friends gained them the name of Stoics.

VIEW IN PALAESTRA

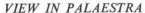

GYMNASIUM

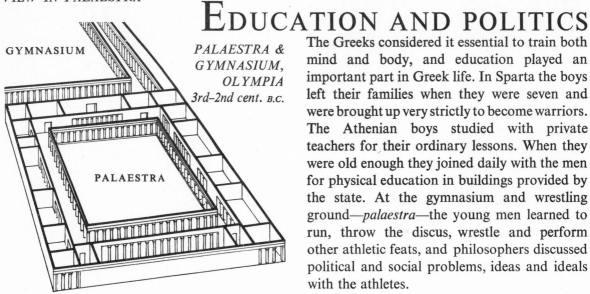

PALAESTRA

*PALAESTRA &
GYMNASIUM,
OLYMPIA
3rd–2nd cent.* B.C.

EDUCATION AND POLITICS

The Greeks considered it essential to train both mind and body, and education played an important part in Greek life. In Sparta the boys left their families when they were seven and were brought up very strictly to become warriors. The Athenian boys studied with private teachers for their ordinary lessons. When they were old enough they joined daily with the men for physical education in buildings provided by the state. At the gymnasium and wrestling ground—*palaestra*—the young men learned to run, throw the discus, wrestle and perform other athletic feats, and philosophers discussed political and social problems, ideas and ideals with the athletes.

26

THE STADIUM, OLYMPIA 4th–2nd cent. B.C.

The earliest buildings were informally grouped, but by the fifth century B.C. they had taken on a more formal rectangular arrangement, as may be seen at Olympia. Accommodation and dressing-rooms were provided for the athletes. The earliest stadia, used for foot races, consisted of a level plain some 210 yards long with starting blocks at one end. Spectators stood or sat on banks on either side. It was not until the fourth or third centuries B.C. that stadia became more architectural in form, as at Delphi.

During the period of the games warfare between city-states was suspended, and all men passed freely through the countryside to the stadia. A victor brought honour to his polis, and was in turn honoured by his fellow citizens.

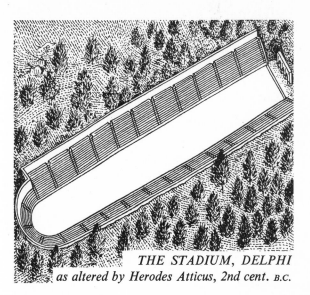

THE STADIUM, DELPHI
as altered by Herodes Atticus, 2nd cent. B.C.

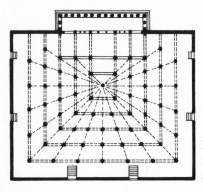

THE COUNCIL HALL, c. 340 B.C. at Megalopolis

While meetings of the general assembly were normally held in the open, meetings of the council took place indoors. The council halls, therefore, were required to seat many citizens, and consequently the Greeks found themselves attempting to solve the problem of roofing buildings which could hold large numbers.

At Eleusis, the first Hall of the Mysteries built in the late sixth century B.C., was one of the earliest buildings in which an attempt was

made to find a solution to this problem. Here the roof was supported by rows of columns like the hypostyle—many columned—hall of an Egyptian temple, but so many columns made it difficult for everyone to see. At Megalopolis (left), the council hall was designed to seat six thousand, and here the columns were arranged radiating outwards from the speaker, so that all the spectators had a clear view of him.

Most council halls, however, were smaller,

seating from six to seven hundred people, and it was possible to support the roof on a few columns; the seats being arranged in a semi-circle as they were in the later theatres (pages 32–33), or following the lines of the walls as in the illustration above, which shows the hall at Priene, built about 200 B.C., where a clear span of more than forty feet was achieved, possibly for the first time. The orator spoke from beside an altar which stood in the middle of the floor.

THE GREEK THEATRE

Drama in Greece developed from songs and dances performed in honour of a god. In early times these religious rites took place on the local threshing floor, in a sacred enclosure or in the agora. In many such places steps were built so that as many people as possible could see what was happening. The theatral area at Knossos has already been noticed (page 5), and similar areas were built in many Cretan agoras (page 20). The important people probably used the steps, while the others stood on the ground or on the surrounding buildings. Steps are to be found adjoining the Erechtheum on the Athenian Acropolis, and alongside the processional way at Eleusis.

All the people of the town and surrounding districts attended the great festivals because of their religious nature, and as the population increased it became necessary to make special provision for the larger audiences. Where there

was a hillside the spectators sat on this, and a flat area—*orchestra*—was built on which the performance was given. Such an arrangement may be seen at Ikaria, in Attica, the home of Thespis, who is credited with having introduced into these songs and dances the first elements of drama as we know it, by the use of an actor. In the fifth or fourth centuries B.C., a simple theatre was built at Ikaria adjoining the agora and the temple. The priests and leading citizens sat in special seats—*prohedria*—at the front, while the rest of the audience either stood, or sat on timber benches. In later theatres the audience had stone seating, often cut out of the solid rock.

Many of the earliest theatres had straight rows of seating facing a rectangular orchestra. At Thorikos three stages of development can be seen by which the simple block of straight seating was extended to seat a growing audience. Extra seats were first added at either side curving round the orchestra to bring the audience as close to the performers as possible. Later when further seats were needed they were added at the back.

During the fifth century B.C., the performance of songs and dances by a group or *chorus* gradually gave way to plays. All the characters were played by men, as no women were allowed to take part. Each actor played several parts, wearing different costumes and masks, so a hut —*skene*—was built adjoining the orchestra where they could change. Originally, as at Thorikos, the skene may have been set to one side, but it was soon moved to a central position so that the actors could make their entrances through doors on to the orchestra.

In Southern Italy, during the fifth century B.C., travelling troupes of comedians used raised timber stages hung around with drapes, and backed by a curtained dressing-room. These they set up in the local agora or in the theatre.

TEMPORARY STAGE FOR COMEDIES

THEATRICAL MASKS 1. *Old man* 2. *Youth* 3. *Old woman* 4. *Young woman*

1. Original 5th cent. rectangular rock-cut seats 2. Curved wings added 3. Rear section of seating added in the 3rd cent. and built above hillside

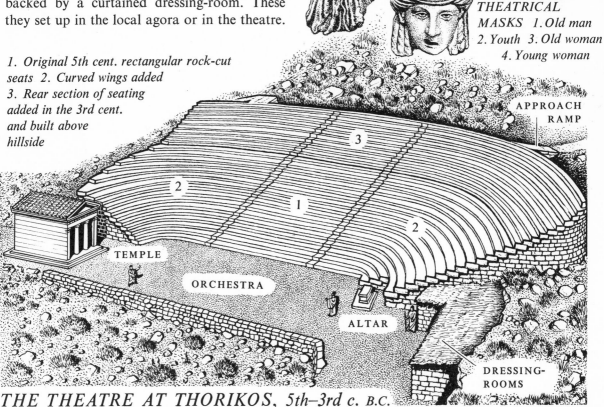

TEMPLE

ORCHESTRA

ALTAR

APPROACH RAMP

DRESSING-ROOMS

THE THEATRE AT THORIKOS, 5th–3rd c. B.C.

31

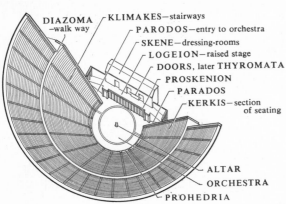

DIAZOMA —walk way

KLIMAKES—stairways

PARODOS—entry to orchestra

SKENE—dressing-rooms

LOGEION—raised stage

DOORS, later THYROMATA

PROSKENION

PARADOS

KERKIS—section of seating

ALTAR

ORCHESTRA

PROHEDRIA

The shape of early orchestras, like that at Thorikos, was not very definite, and perhaps the circle of the threshing floor may have suggested a more satisfying form, especially as it enabled as many people as possible to be seated close to the performers. A typical Greek theatre after the third century B.C. shows the perfection that the Greeks looked for in their buildings. The auditorium was divided into blocks of seats by a horizontal walking way and stairways: the

Greek names for the various parts of the theatre may be seen on the small drawing.

The orchestra of beaten earth, with a central altar, was backed by the skene. In front of this was a colonnaded building—*proskenion*—the roof of which was used as a stage or speaking place. Three doorways in the skene led to the stage, and entrances could also be made from either end. The central doorway represented the home of the chief character, and the other doors were the homes of the minor characters. While the actors performed on this upper level, the chorus remained in the orchestra, which was approached by entry ways between the ends of the seating and the skene. In later theatres, as above, the three doors were replaced by a number of openings—*thyromata*. Painted scenery was used in these openings and between the columns of the proskenion. The whole performance took place in the hours of daylight.

TYPICAL HOUSE AT OLYNTHUS, 4th cent. B.C.

It is part of a block of ten houses which was repeated throughout the grid-iron pattern of the town

LEFT: General view of the house from the south

BELOW: Cut open drawing showing the ground floor rooms

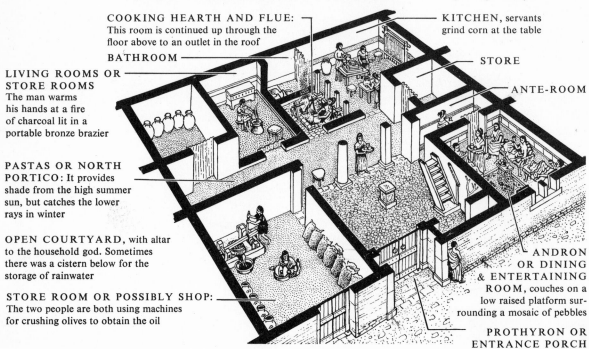

COOKING HEARTH AND FLUE: This room is continued up through the floor above to an outlet in the roof

BATHROOM

LIVING ROOMS OR STORE ROOMS The man warms his hands at a fire of charcoal lit in a portable bronze brazier

PASTAS OR NORTH PORTICO: It provides shade from the high summer sun, but catches the lower rays in winter

OPEN COURTYARD, with altar to the household god. Sometimes there was a cistern below for the storage of rainwater

STORE ROOM OR POSSIBLY SHOP: The two people are both using machines for crushing olives to obtain the oil

KITCHEN, servants grind corn at the table

STORE

ANTE-ROOM

ANDRON OR DINING & ENTERTAINING ROOM, couches on a low raised platform surrounding a mosaic of pebbles

PROTHYRON OR ENTRANCE PORCH

THE GREEK HOUSE

As late as the third century B.C., the megaron type house with its main hall facing a colonnaded courtyard was still being used in Asia Minor. On mainland Greece, however, a different form of house had developed for both rich and poor alike, varying only in size and finish. In northern Greece, the greater part of the city of Olynthus has been excavated, and it is possible to see what the houses may have been like.

Every house looked inward to a private courtyard, turning its back on the town. A gated porch in the southern wall led into the courtyard, which was usually cobbled, and had an altar to the household god in the middle. Sometimes there was a cistern underneath the court to store rainwater. Timber stairs led to an upper gallery off which the bedrooms opened. To the north of the courtyard, at ground-level, was a long portico—*pastas*—behind which were the domestic quarters. These included a unit which combined a bathroom, women's working room and a cooking room with a large hearth. This room was continued up through the floor above to the roof where a hole allowed the smoke to escape.

In many Olynthus houses quantities of loom weights were found in the women's working room next to the cooking room, suggesting that it was here that the lady of the house carried out her weaving, instructed her daughters in the art and supervised the slave girls who helped her. It must certainly have been the warmest room in the house, and was probably used for general living in winter-time.

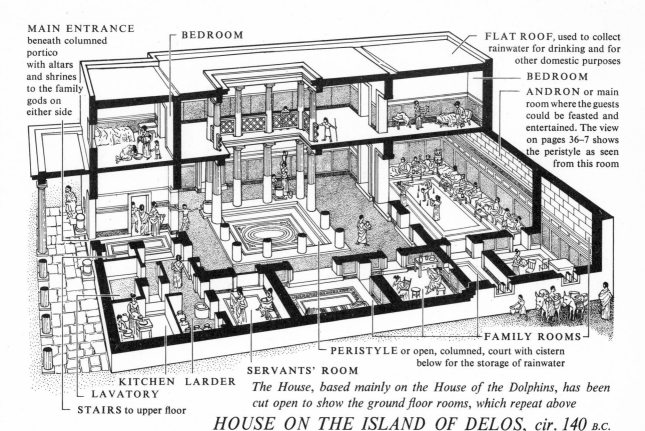

MAIN ENTRANCE beneath columned portico with altars and shrines to the family gods on either side

BEDROOM

FLAT ROOF, used to collect rainwater for drinking and for other domestic purposes

BEDROOM

ANDRON or main room where the guests could be feasted and entertained. The view on pages 36–7 shows the peristyle as seen from this room

FAMILY ROOMS

PERISTYLE or open, columned, court with cistern below for the storage of rainwater

SERVANTS' ROOM

KITCHEN LARDER

LAVATORY

STAIRS to upper floor

The House, based mainly on the House of the Dolphins, has been cut open to show the ground floor rooms, which repeat above

HOUSE ON THE ISLAND OF DELOS, cir. 140 B.C.

Apart from the normal domestic duties, the Grecian wife had to supervise the pressing of the olives to obtain their oil. A special machine for this purpose was set up in one of the side rooms opening off the courtyard. The oil, which was used for cooking and also in lamps, was stored in large jars. The corn was stored in the driest room in the house, and the wine in the coolest.

Opening off the courtyard and entered through an ante-room was the main room—*andron*. In the better houses the andron floor was decorated with a pebble mosaic and was surrounded by a low cement platform built along the walls. These were stuccoed and painted in panels of red, white and yellow. The traditional building materials were still used, mud brick walls on stone bases, with timber posts and beams and tile roofs. Similar houses existed in Athens, but the fifth century B.C. working-class houses were very much simpler, although each still had its own courtyard off

which the rooms and workshop opened, as can be seen from those excavated near the Agora.

The houses on the island of Delos, see illustration above, date mainly from the third and second centuries B.C. They were generally better than those of Olynthus. More rooms had mosaic floors and mosaics decorated the courtyards, which were surrounded by marble colonnades. During the day the courtyard was used whenever possible, or the pastas when shade was needed. In the evenings the host would receive his guests in the andron, offering them couches with cushions to lie on. His treasured vases and the decoration of the room were the subjects of their admiration. Small three-legged tables were set beside the couches. Servants brought food and bowls of water, for hands were washed both before and after the meal. When the tables were removed, an entertainment might be given by professional dancing girls. The women of the house remained in their own quarters while male guests were in the house.

1. Funerary stele 2. The sacrificial calf, cir. 570 B.C. 3. Bronze bull 4. Athenian coin 5. Skyphos, late 5th cent.
6. House mosaic, Olynthus, 4th cent. B.C. 7. Terracotta knucklebone player, cir. 300 B.C. 8. Vase, cir. 460 B.C.

In democratic Greece, when there were no longer any kings, the need for the great tholos tombs (page 7) ceased. The *necropolis*—city of the dead—or cemetery of classical times consisted of family vaults, for the Greeks liked to remain within the family circle even after death. Over the vault, sculpture or a simple funerary stone—*stele*—was erected. The stele might be decorated with a relief showing the dead person, often looking at some member of the family or at a treasured possession. Soldiers who fell in battle were buried by the state in a common grave covered by a simple mound, such as may still be seen at Marathon.

It has been possible to discover a great deal about the way in which the people of Ancient Greece lived from the buildings which we have shown you. Archaeologists have not only unearthed and restored many different types of buildings, but have also found sculptures, statues, votive offerings, mosaics, vases and domestic utensils. The paintings on the vases show us scenes of daily life and also scenes of military prowess and religious significance. All of these things, together with the writings of poets, playwrights and philosophers, have enabled us to build up our pictures of the life of these ancient people.

Visitors to the country may see for themselves the remains of monuments, temples, shrines, theatres and houses, and the pictures in this book may help you to visualize how they looked, and also to appreciate the great debt that modern civilization owes to Greece.

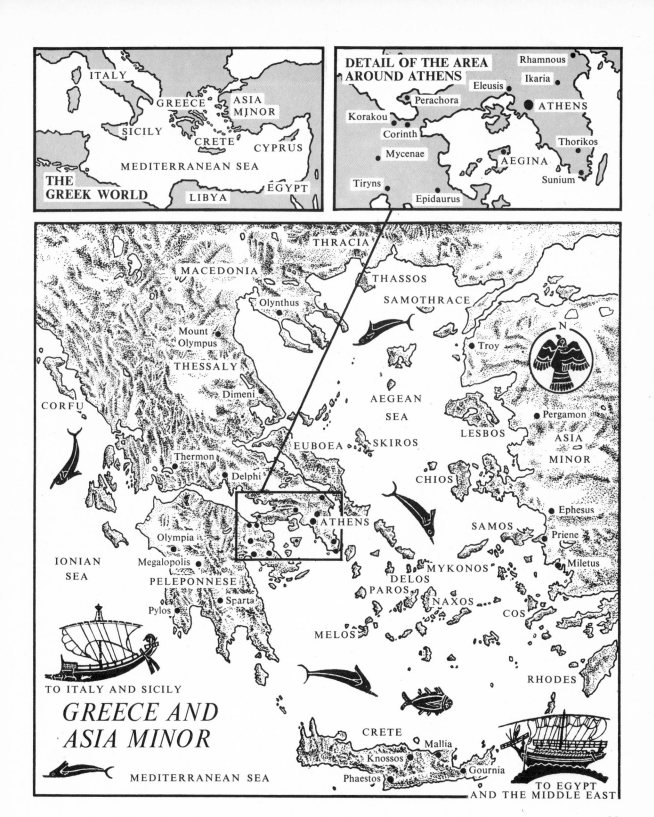

THE GREEK WORLD

ITALY
GREECE
ASIA MINOR
SICILY
CRETE
CYPRUS
MEDITERRANEAN SEA
EGYPT
LIBYA

DETAIL OF THE AREA AROUND ATHENS

Rhamnous
Eleusis
Ikaria
Perachora
ATHENS
Korakou
Corinth
Mycenae
Thorikos
AEGINA
Tiryns
Sunium
Epidaurus

GREECE AND ASIA MINOR

THRACIA
MACEDONIA
THASSOS
SAMOTHRACE
Olynthus
Mount Olympus
Troy
THESSALY
Dimeni
AEGEAN SEA
Pergamon
CORFU
ASIA MINOR
EUBOEA
SKIROS
LESBOS
Thermon
CHIOS
Delphi
ATHENS
Ephesus
SAMOS
Priene
Olympia
Miletus
Megalopolis
MYKONOS
PELEPONNESE
DELOS
Miletus
IONIAN SEA
PAROS
NAXOS
COS
Pylos
Sparta
MELOS
RHODES
TO ITALY AND SICILY
CRETE
Mallia
Knossos
Gournia
MEDITERRANEAN SEA
Phaestos
TO EGYPT AND THE MIDDLE EAST

N

INDEX

ACKNOWLEDGMENTS

The authors would like to thank the American School of Classical Studies, Athens, and Professor Homer A. Thompson; the Royal Ontario Museum, Canada, and Professor J. Walter Graham; the National Archaeological Museum, Athens; and the British Museum, for help, advice, or the use of material from their collections or publications.

Thanks are also due to all those who have helped with criticism and advice, and to the many authors whose works or excavation reports have formed the background to this study of Ancient Greece. They would also like to thank their son, Robert, for his patient photographic work, which formed the basis for many of the reconstructions.

Co-published by Brockhampton Press Ltd, Leicester, England, and William R. Scott Inc., New York, U.S.A.
Printed in Great Britain by Jarrold & Sons Ltd, Norwich